ROD STEWART

Selections from
THE GREAT AMERICAN SONGBOOK
Volumes I, II, III

International Music Publications Limited

Arrangements and engraving: Artemis Music Limited
(www.artemismusic.com)
Photograph courtesy of London Features International

Published 2004

International
MUSIC
Publications

RESPECT
THE VALUE OF
MUSIC

As Time Goes By 4

Baby It's Cold Outside 14

Blue Moon 20

But Not For Me 26

Embraceable You 9

Ev'ry Time We Say Goodbye 32

(I Love You) For Sentimental Reasons 37

I Can't Get Started 42

I'm In The Mood For Love 46

It Had To Be You 50

Kiss To Build A Dream On 60

Manhattan 55

Night And Day 66

A Nightingale Sang In Berkeley Square 70

Stardust 75

S'Wonderful 80

They Can't Take That Away From Me 84

The Way You Look Tonight 88

What A Wonderful World 92

You Belong To Me 97

AS TIME GOES BY

Words and Music by Herman Hupfeld

Redwood Music Ltd, London NW1 8BD (for Commonwealth Of Nations, Eire, Germany, Austria, Switzerland, Spain and South Africa only)
Warner/Chappell Music Ltd, London W6 8BS (for World excl. Commonwealth Of Nations, Eire, Germany, Austria, Switzerland, Spain and South Africa)

lax, re - lieve the ten - sion. *R:*And no mat - ter what the pro - gress, *QL:*or what may yet be proved, *R:* the

sim - ple facts of a life are such, *Both:* they can - not be re - moved. *R:*You must re - mem - ber this, a
when two lov - ers woo, they

kiss is____ still a kiss, a sigh is____ just a sigh. The
still say____ "I love you", on that you____ can re - ly. *Both:* No

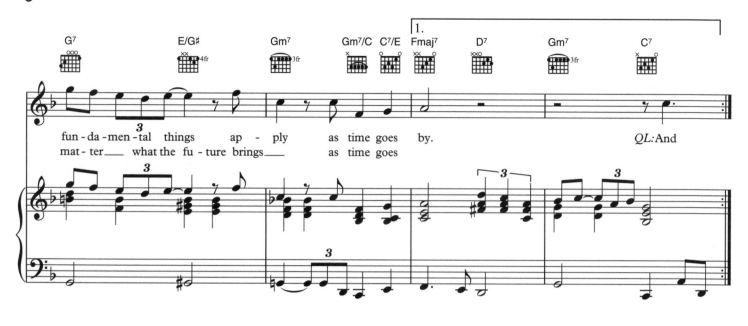

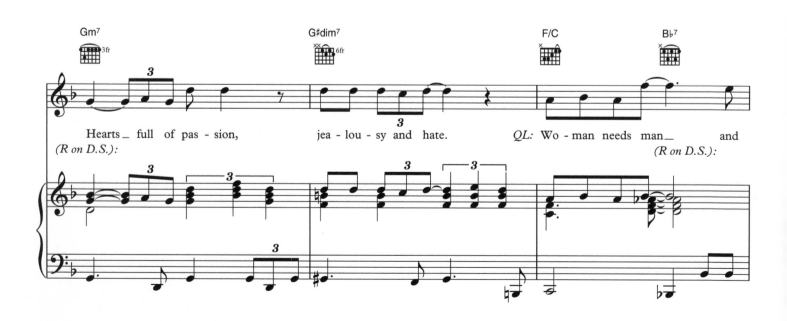

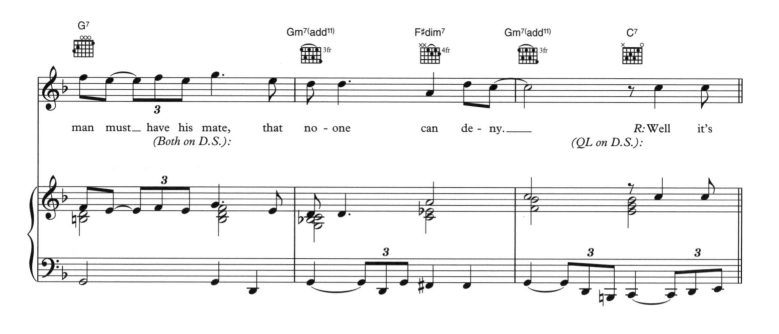

man must__ have his mate, that no-one can de-ny.____ *R:* Well it's

(Both on D.S.): *(QL on D.S.):*

still the same old sto-ry, a fight for love and glo-ry, a case of do or die.

(QL on D.S.):

To Coda

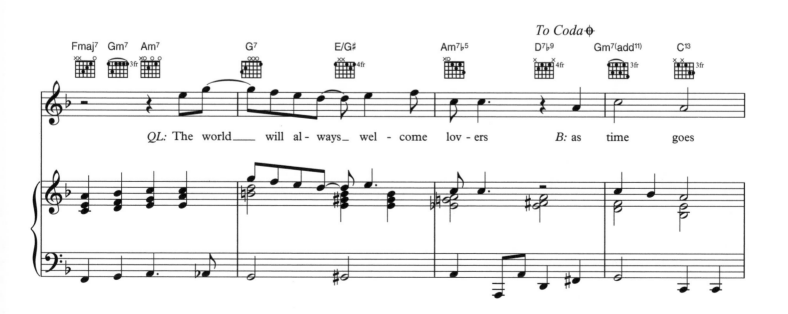

QL: The world____ will al-ways__ wel-come lov-ers *B:* as time goes

Embraceable You

Music and Lyrics by George Gershwin and Ira Gershwin

To Coda

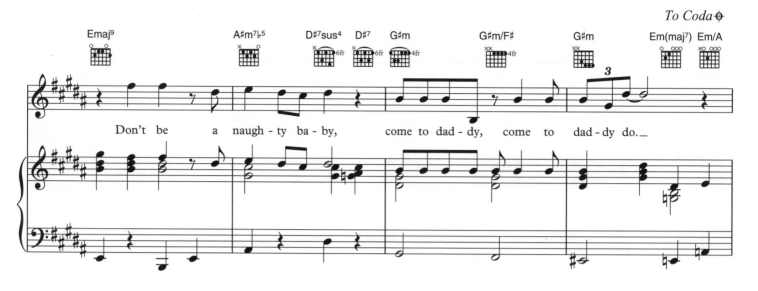

Don't be a naugh-ty ba-by, come to dad-dy, come to dad-dy do._

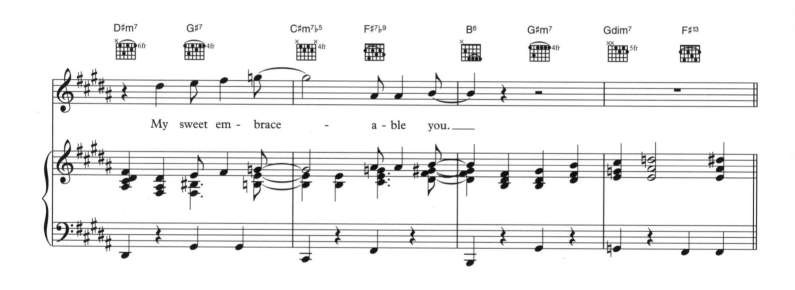

My sweet em - brace - a - ble you.___

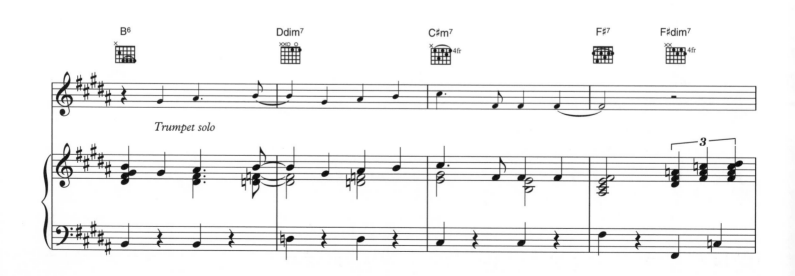

Trumpet solo

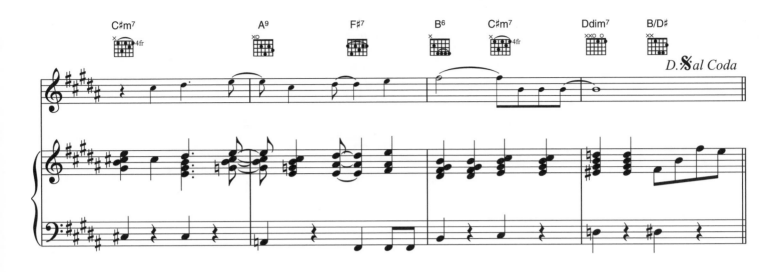

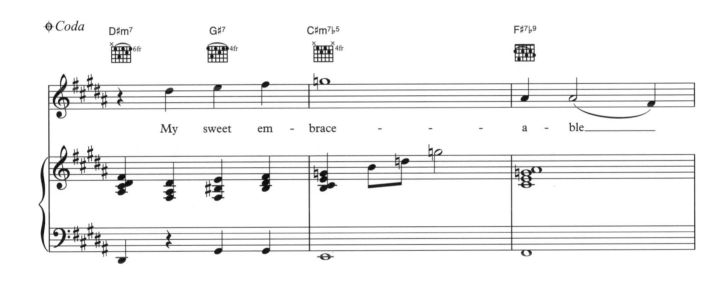

My sweet em - brace - - a - ble_____

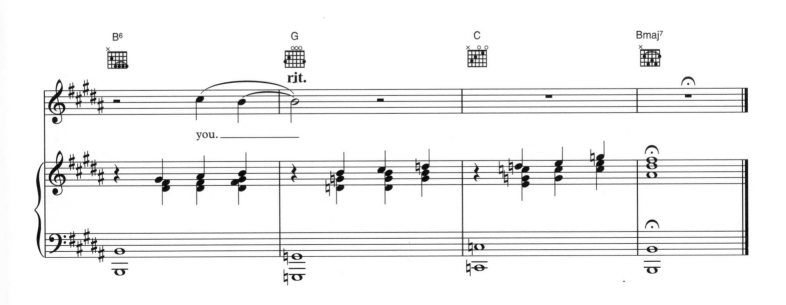

you._____

rit.

BABY IT'S COLD OUTSIDE

Words and Music by Frank Loesser

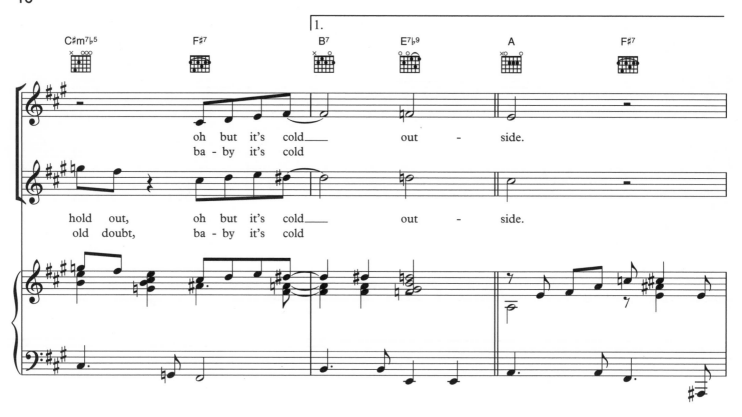

oh but it's cold____ out - side.
ba - by it's cold

hold out, oh but it's cold____ out - side.
old doubt, ba - by it's cold

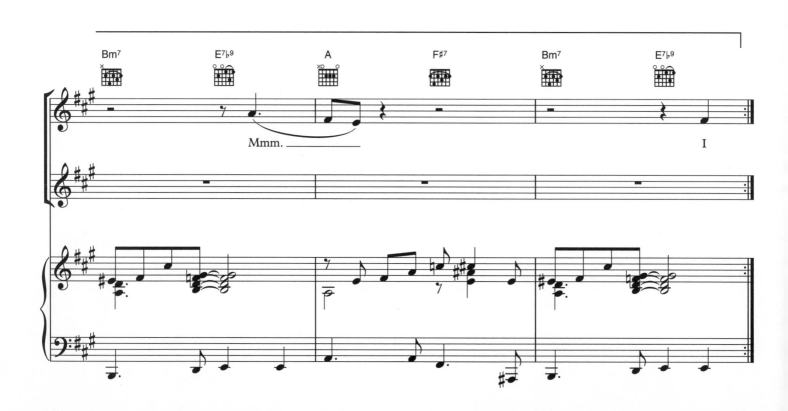

Mmm. _____

BLUE MOON

Words by Lorenz Hart
Music by Richard Rodgers

Once up-on a time, be - fore I took up smil - ing, I hat - ed the moon - light.

Shad - ows of the night that po - ets find be - guil - ing seemed flat as the moon - light.

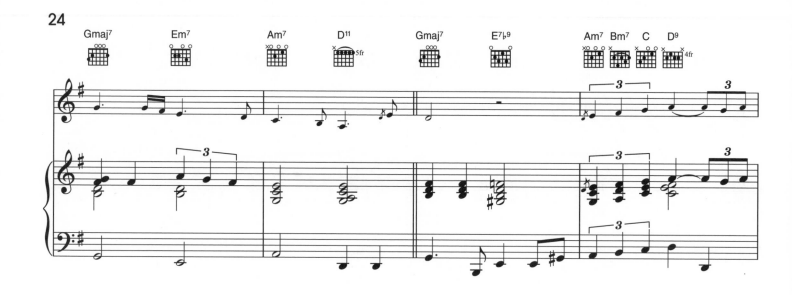

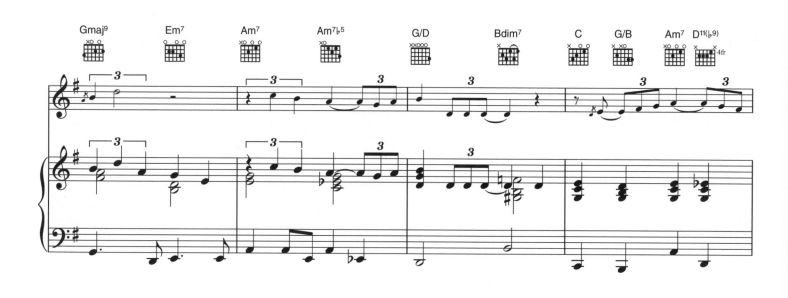

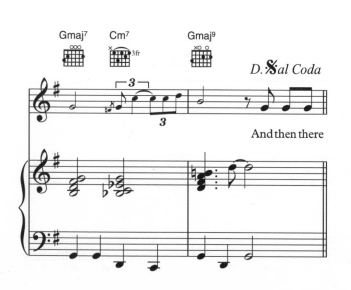

D. S al Coda

And then there

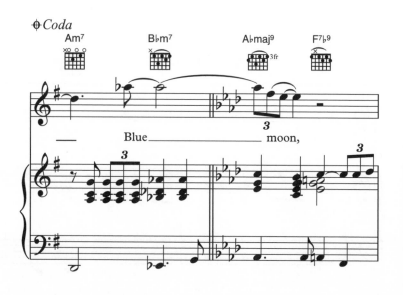

Coda

Blue _____ moon,

BUT NOT FOR ME

Music & Lyrics by George Gershwin and Ira Gershwin

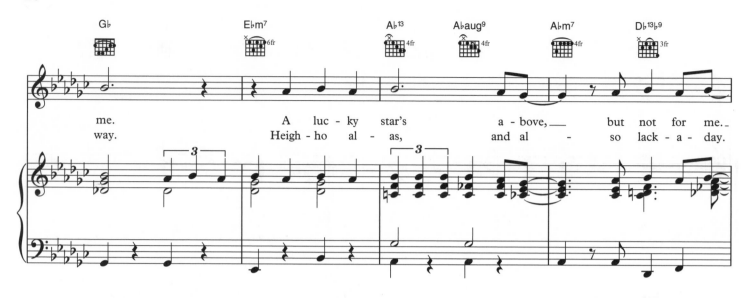

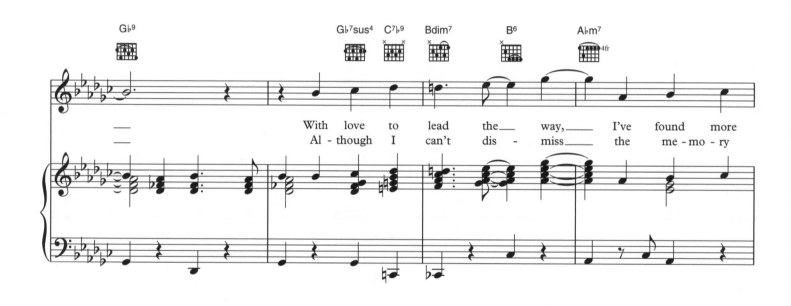

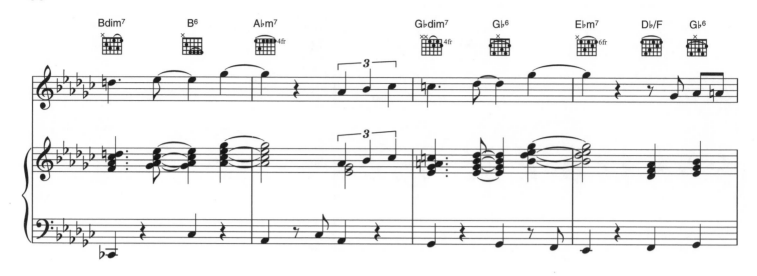

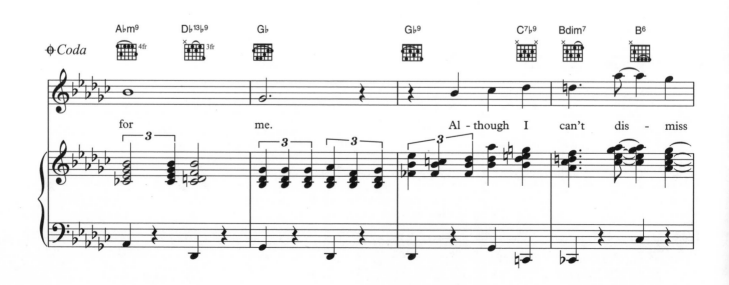

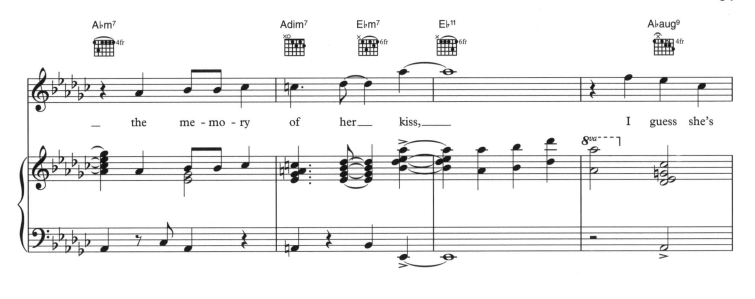

the me-mo-ry of her kiss, I guess she's

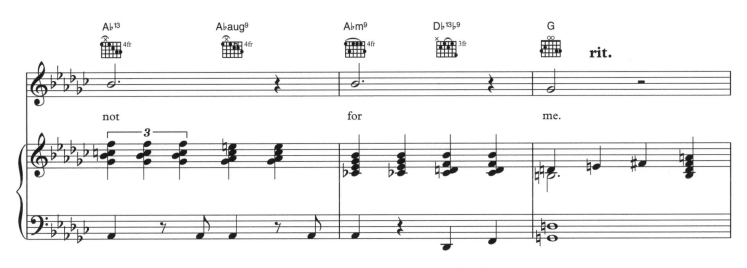

not for me.

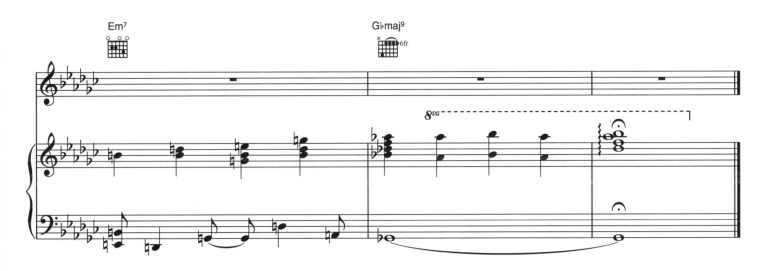

Verse 3:
It all began so well, but what an end.
This is the time a feller needs a friend.
The climax of the plot should be a marriage knot,
But there's no knot for me.

Although I can't...

EV'RY TIME WE SAY GOODBYE

Words and Music by Cole Porter

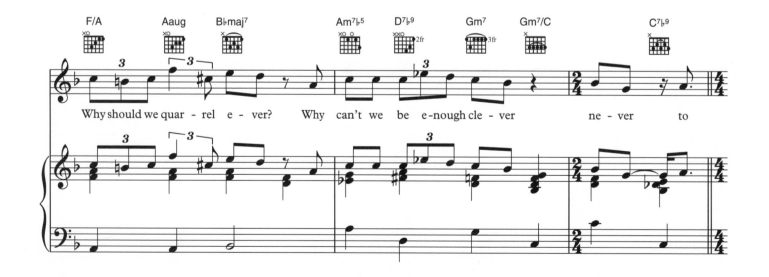

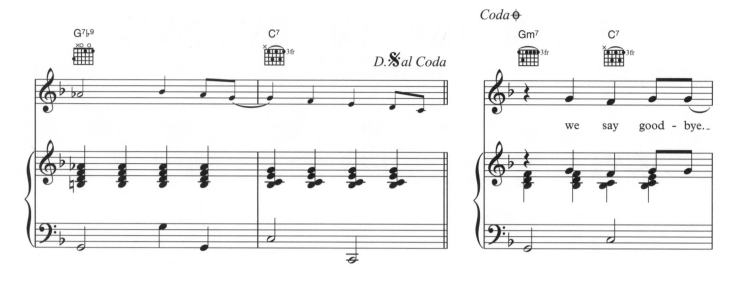

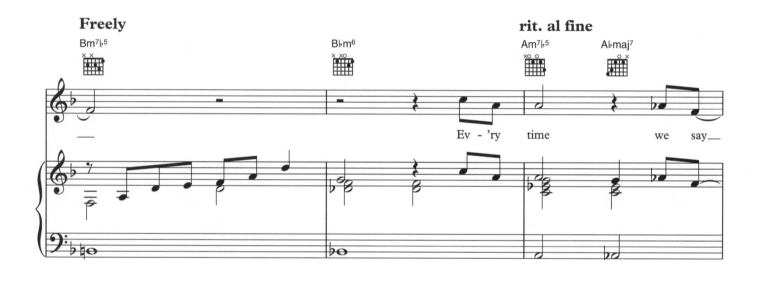

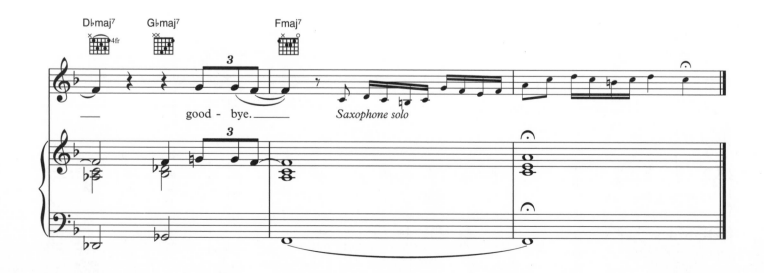

(I LOVE YOU)
FOR SENTIMENTAL REASONS

Words by Derek Watson
Music by William Best

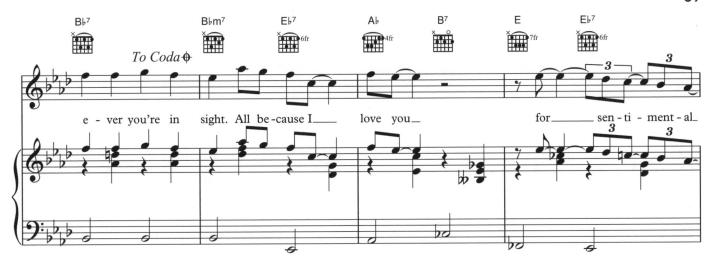

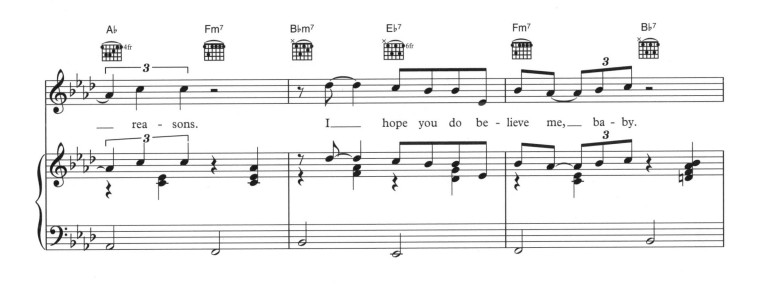

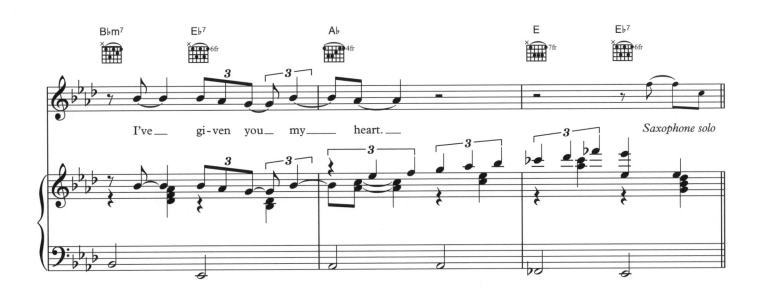

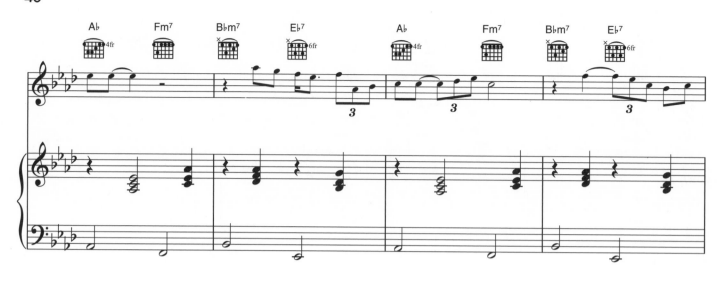

D.%al Coda

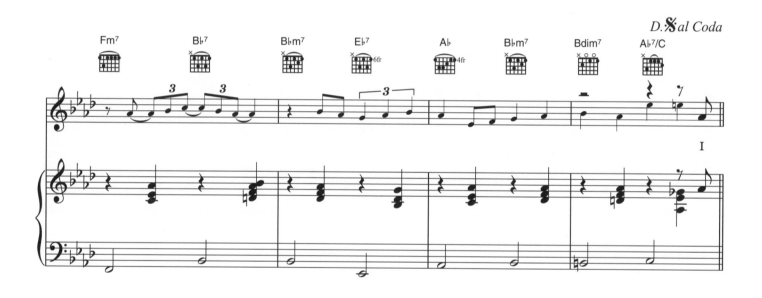

Coda ⊕

sight. All be-cause I_____ love you__ for__ sen - ti - ment-al__

I Can't Get Started

Words by Ira Gershwin
Music by Vernon Duke

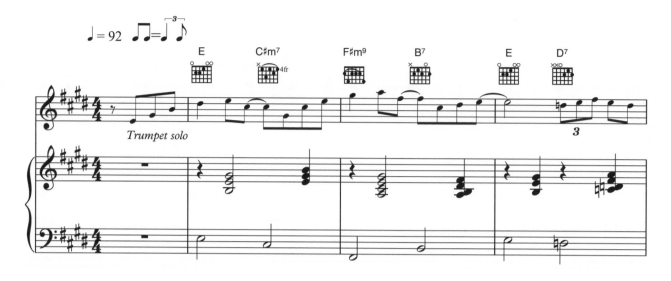

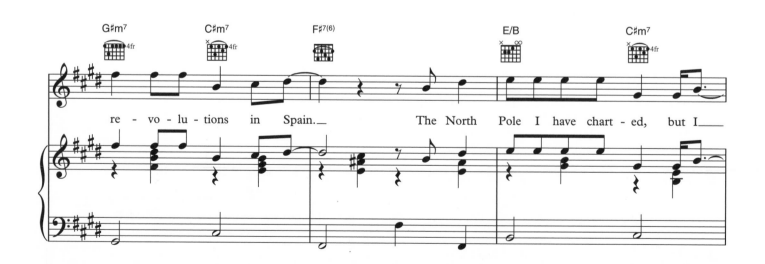

I'M IN THE MOOD FOR LOVE

Words by Dorothy Fields
Music by Jimmy McHugh

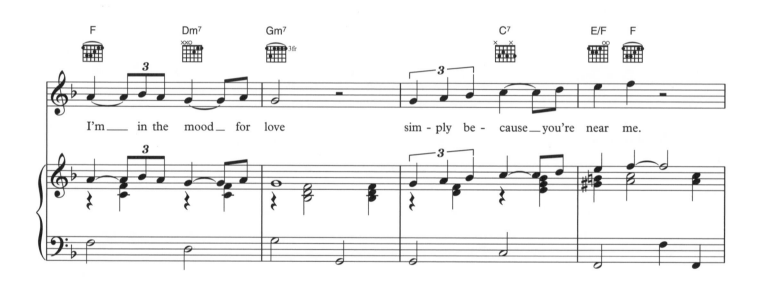

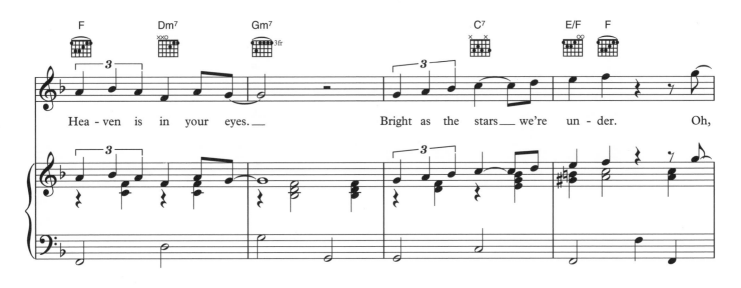

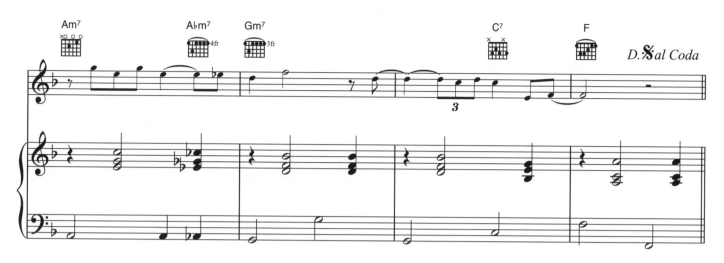

D.%al Coda

Coda

get it. 'Cause I'm _____ in the mood for love.

Freely

I'm _____ in the mood for love. _____ for love, _____ for love. _____

IT HAD TO BE YOU

Words by Gus Kahn
Music by Isham Jones

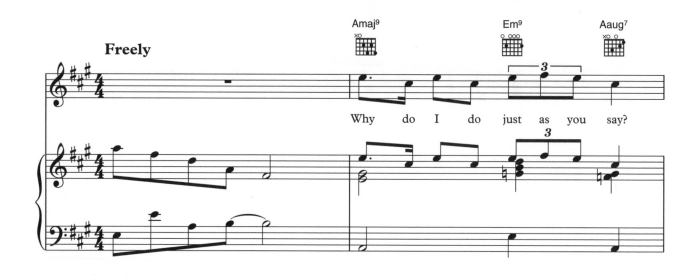

won-der-ful you,___ it___ had to be you.___

Saxophone solo

won-der-ful you,___ it___ had to be you.

MANHATTAN

Words by Lorenz Hart
Music by Richard Rodgers

58

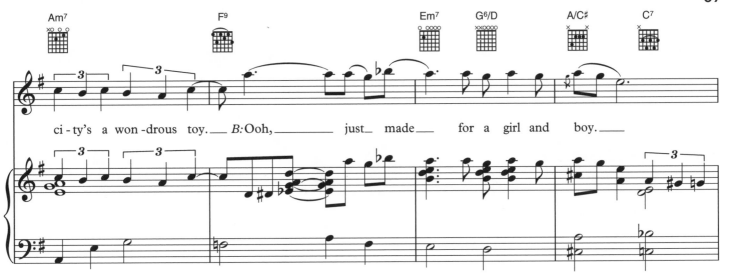

ci - ty's a won-drous toy.___ *B:* Ooh, _____ just___ made___ for a girl and boy.___

Both: We'll turn Man-hat-tan in - to an isle___ of joy.

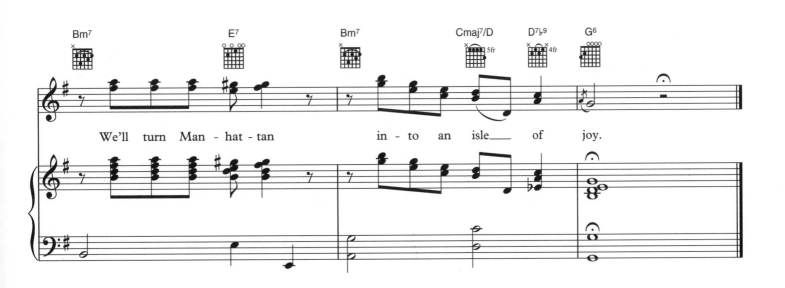

We'll turn Man-hat-tan in - to an isle___ of joy.

KISS TO BUILD A DREAM ON

Words and Music by Oscar Hammerstein II, Bert Kalmar and Harry Ruby

Give me a kiss to__ build a dream on, And my i - ma - gi - na - tion will thrive u - pon that
Give me a kiss be - fore you leave me, And my i - ma - gi - na - tion will feed my hun - gry

kiss.
heart.

Sweet - heart,   I   ask   no more than this,
Leave   me   one   thing be - fore   we   part,

A kiss to build a

1.

dream on.

2.

dream on.

When I'm__ a - lone

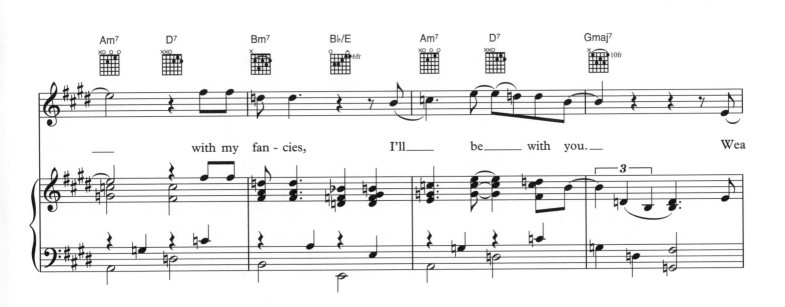

___   with my fan - cies,   I'll____ be_____ with you.___

Wea

-ving ro - man - ces, And ma - king be - lieve they're all true.__ So__

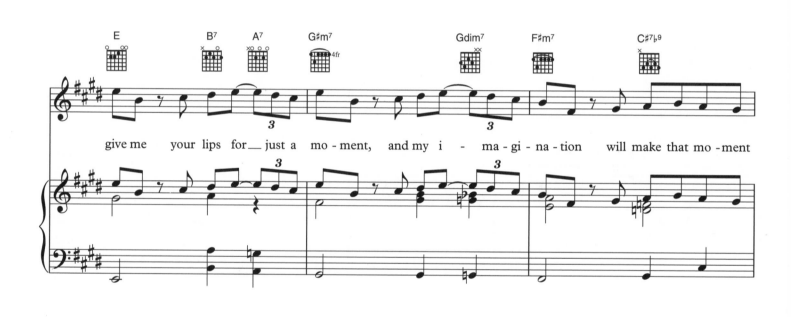

give me your lips for__ just a mo - ment, and my i - ma - gi - na - tion will make that mo - ment

live. Well give me what you a - lone can give, a kiss to build a

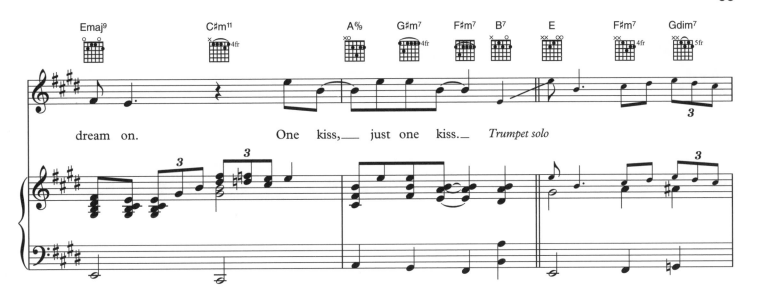

dream on.   One kiss,___ just one kiss.___ *Trumpet solo*

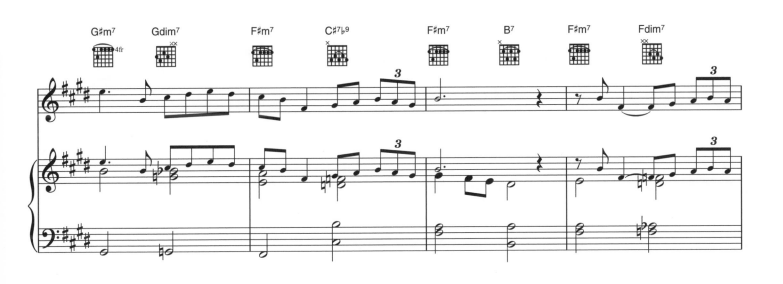

When I'm a - lone___   with all my

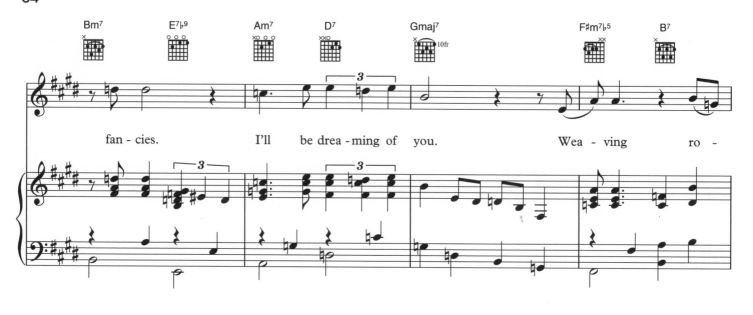

fan - cies.   I'll   be drea - ming of   you.   Wea - ving   ro -

man - ces,   and   ma - king be - lieve they're all   true.___   So____

give me   your lips for___ just a   mo - ment,   and my i - ma - gi - na - tion   will make that mo - ment

live._____ Please give me what you a-lone can give, A kiss to build a dream on.

A kiss to build a dream on._____ Just a kiss to build a dream on.

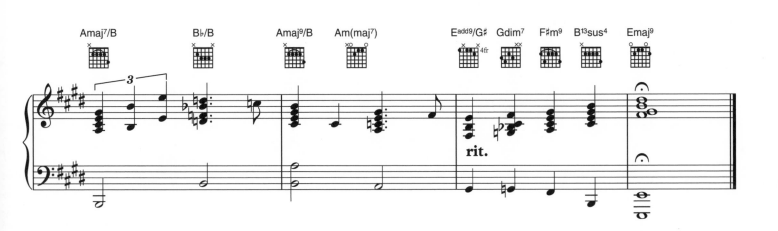

NIGHT AND DAY

Words and Music by Cole Porter

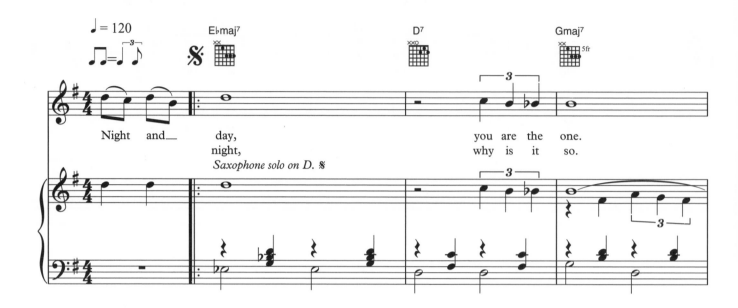

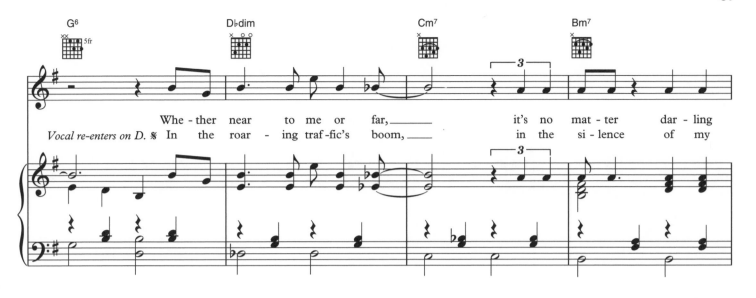

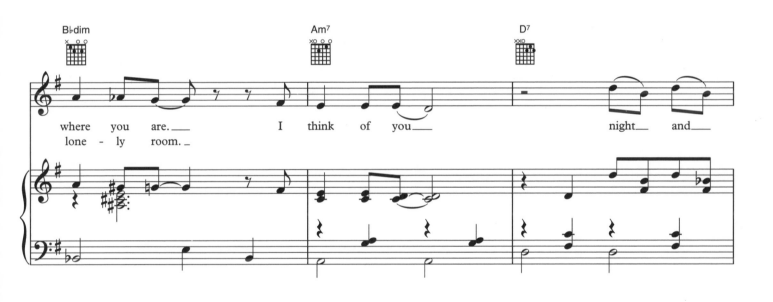

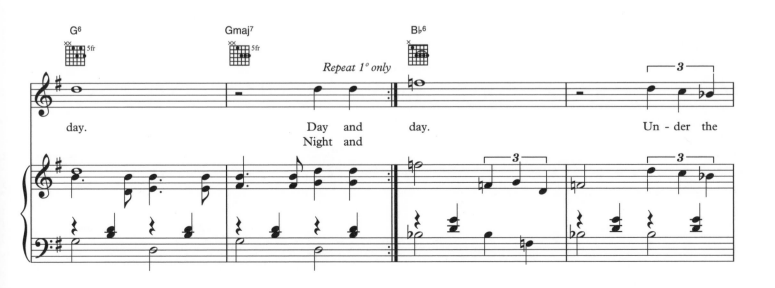

hide of me _____ there's an oh such a hun- gry yearn- ing burn- ing in-

side of me. _____ And this tor- ment won't be through 'til you

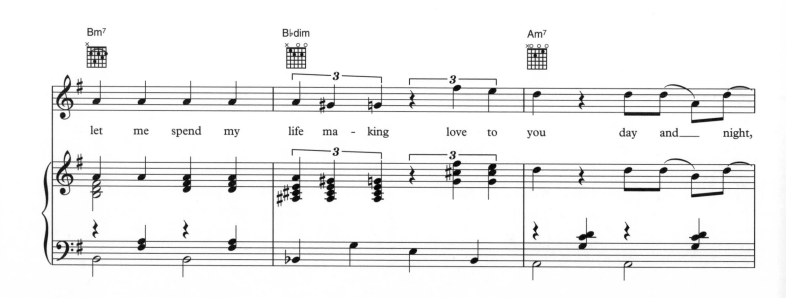

let me spend my life ma- king love to you day and___ night,

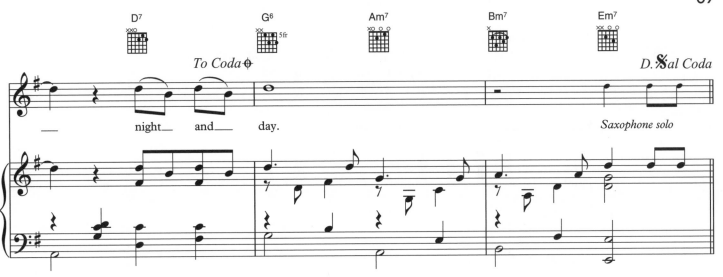

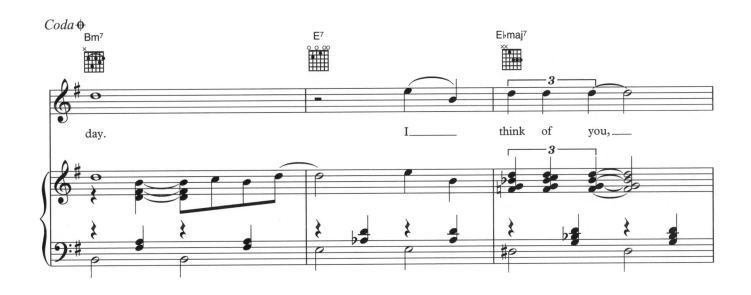

A Nightingale Sang in Berkeley Square

Words by Eric Maschwitz
Music by Manning Sherwin

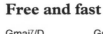

Free and fast

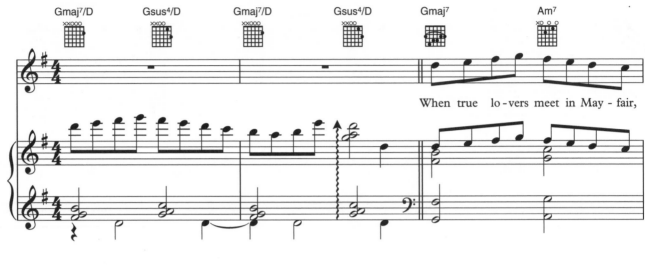

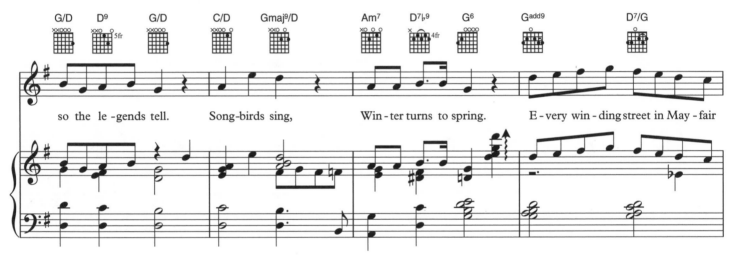

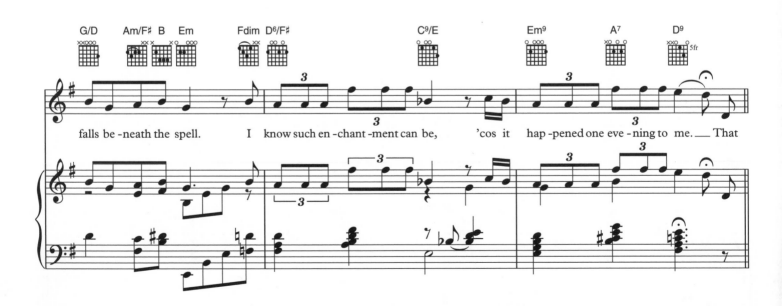

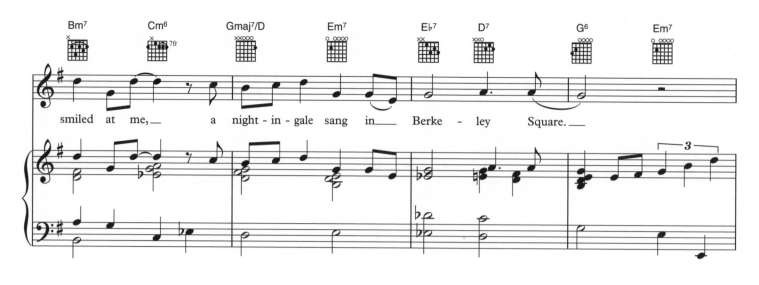

smiled at me, __ a night-in-gale sang in __ Berke-ley Square. __

The moon that lin-gered o-ver Lon-don town, __
When dawn came stea-ling up all gold and blue, to

poor puz-zled moon, __ he wore a frown. How could he know we two were
in-ter-rupt __ our ren-dez-vous. __ I still re-mem-ber how-you

so in love. The whole darn__ world__ seemed up - side down.__ The
smiled and said "Was that a__ dream or was it true?"__ Our

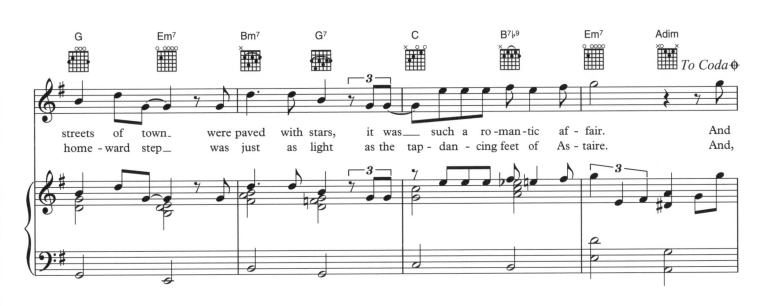

streets of town__ were paved with stars, it was__ such a ro-man-tic af - fair. And
home - ward step__ was just as light as the tap - dan - cing feet of As - taire. And,

as we kissed and said good - night, a night - in - gale sang in__ Berke - ley Square.

Violin solo

Coda

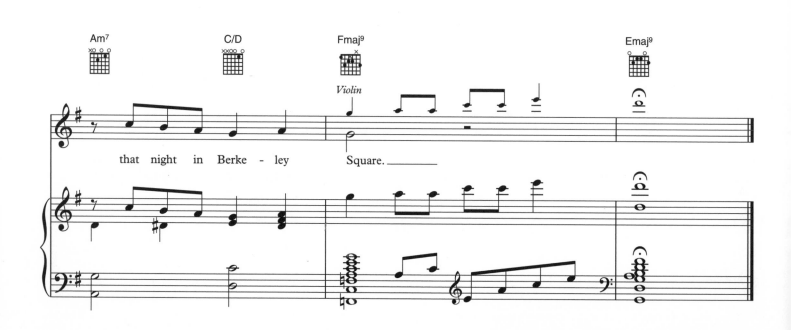

Stardust

Words by Mitchell Parish
Music by Hoagy Carmichael

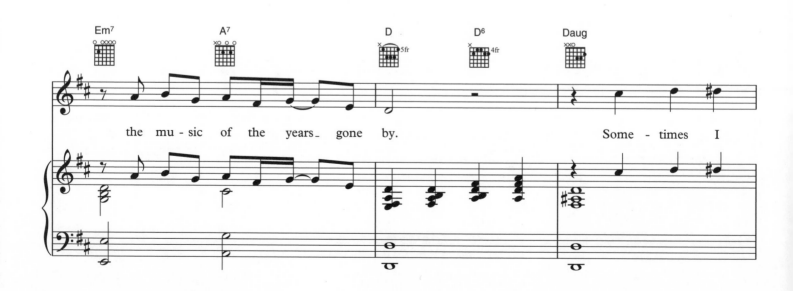

A tempo ♩ = 100

won - der   why I spend   the lone - ly   nights   dream - ing of a song.

Trumpet solo 2°

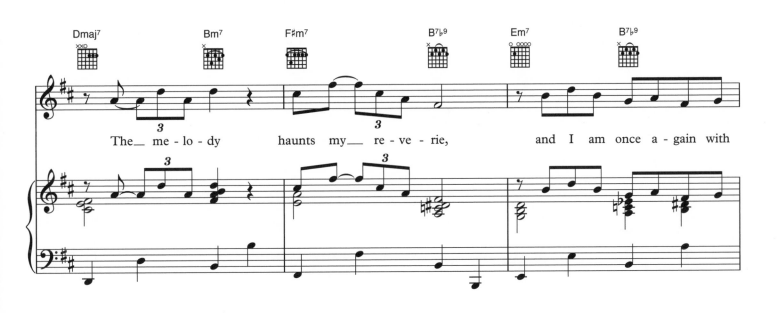

The_ me - lo - dy   haunts my_ re - ve - rie,   and I am once a - gain with

you.   When our   love_ was   new,   And each kiss an in - spi -

Trumpet

Vocal re-enters 2°

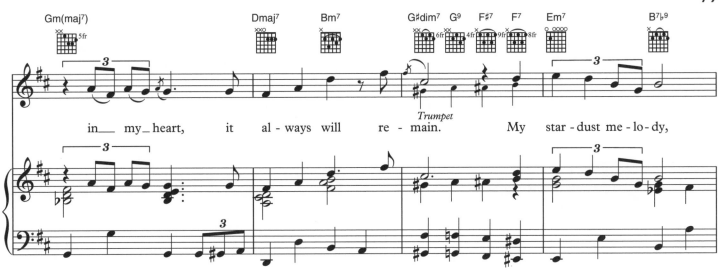

in___ my__ heart, it al-ways will re-main. My star-dust me-lo-dy,

the___ me-mo-ry of love's re-frain.___

Trumpet solo

the me-mo-ry of love's re-frain._____

S'WONDERFUL

Music and Lyrics by George Gershwin and Ira Gershwin

83

THEY CAN'T TAKE THAT AWAY FROM ME

Music and Lyrics by George Gershwin and Ira Gershwin

knife, the way we danced 'til three. The way you changed my life,

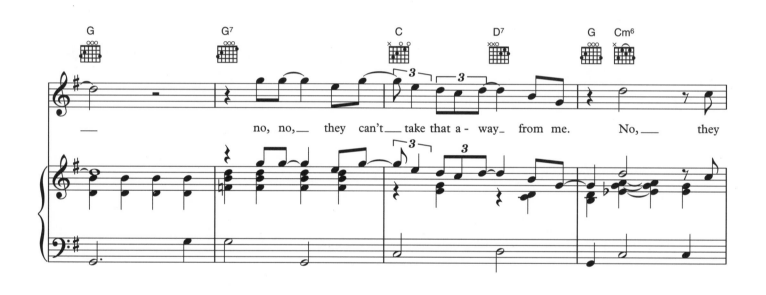

— no, no,___ they can't___ take that a-way_ from me. No,___ they

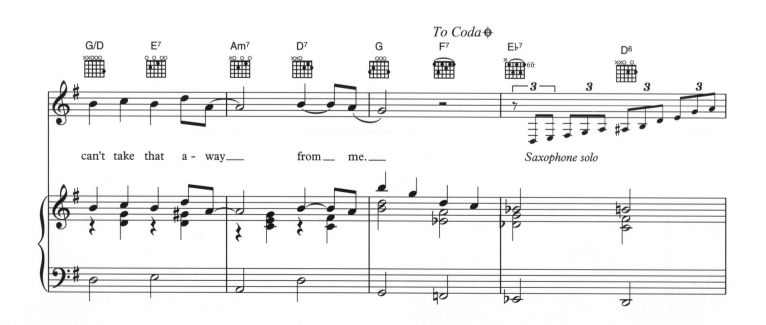

To Coda

can't take that a-way___ from_ me.___

Saxophone solo

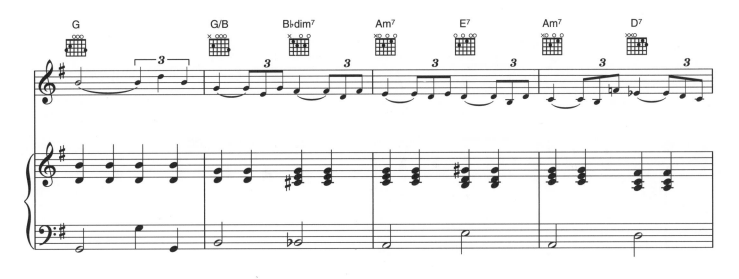

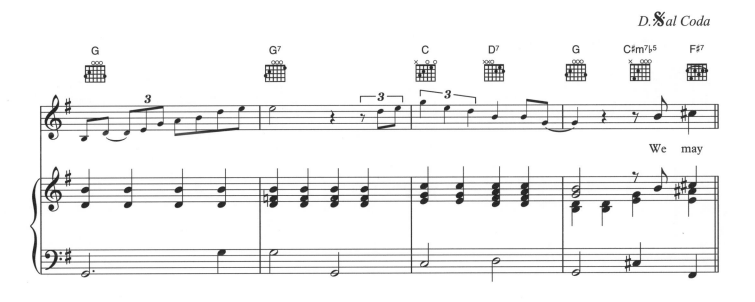

The Way You Look Tonight

Words by Dorothy Fields
Music by Jerome Kern

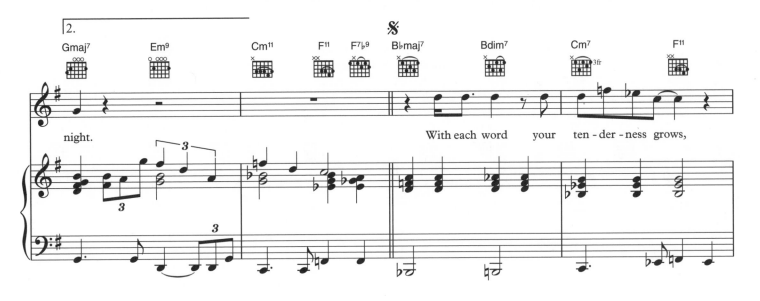

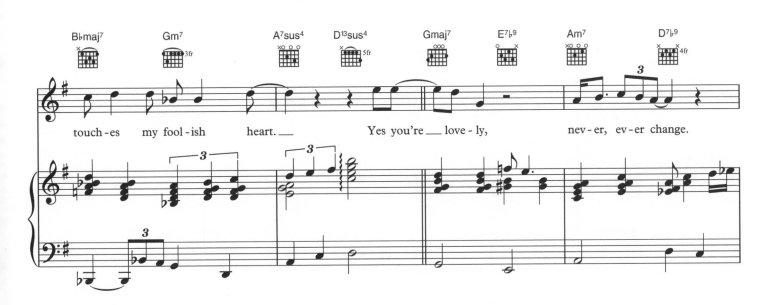

Keep that breath - less charm, won't you__ please ar - range it, 'cause I love you

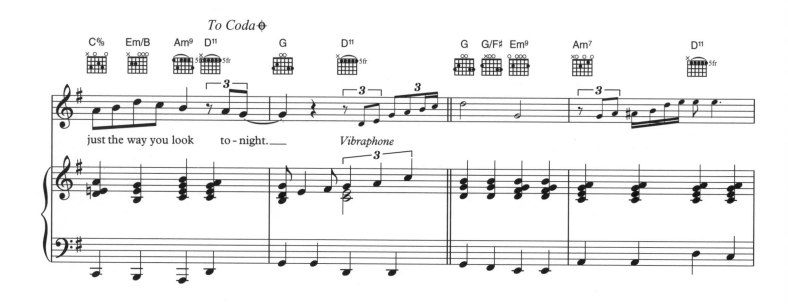

To Coda

just the way you look to - night.__ *Vibraphone*

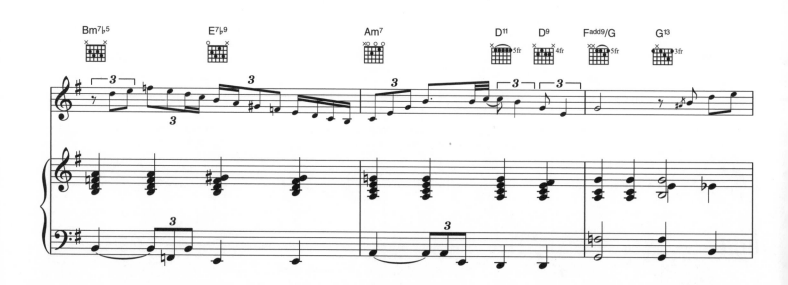

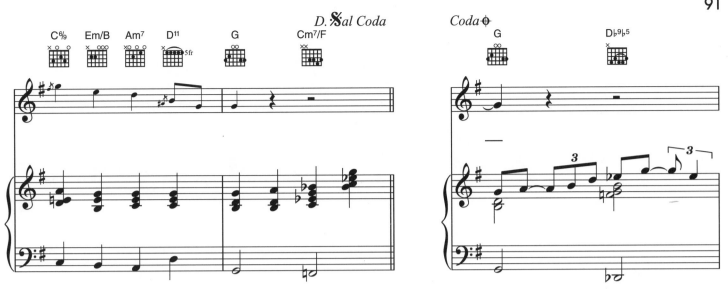

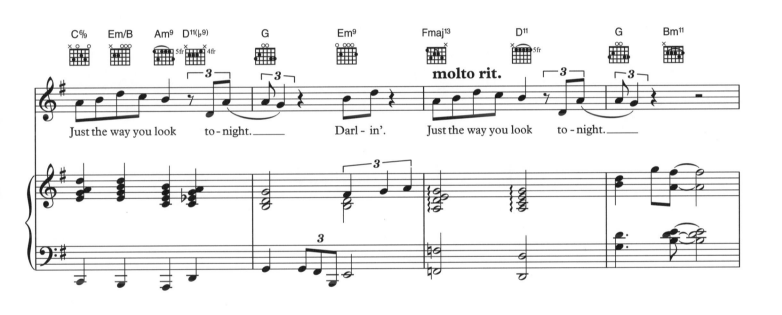

Just the way you look to-night.____ Darl - in'. Just the way you look to-night.____

molto rit.

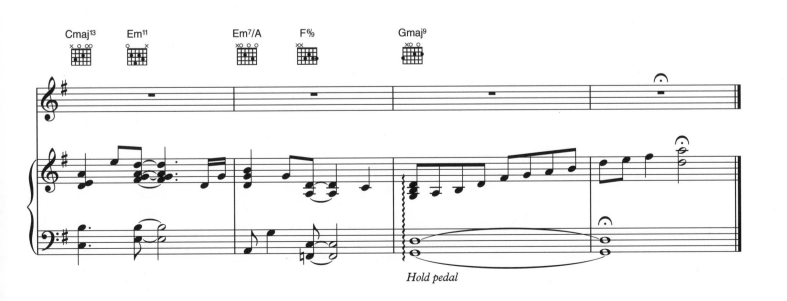

Hold pedal

WHAT A WONDERFUL WORLD

Words and Music by George Weiss and Bob Thiele

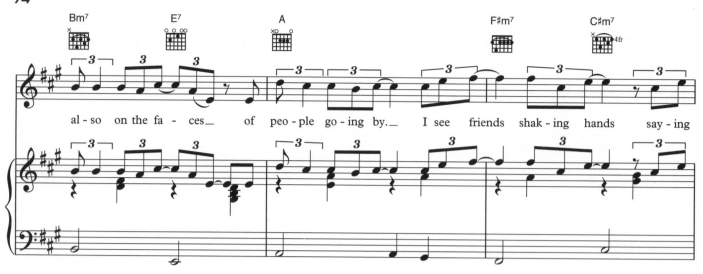

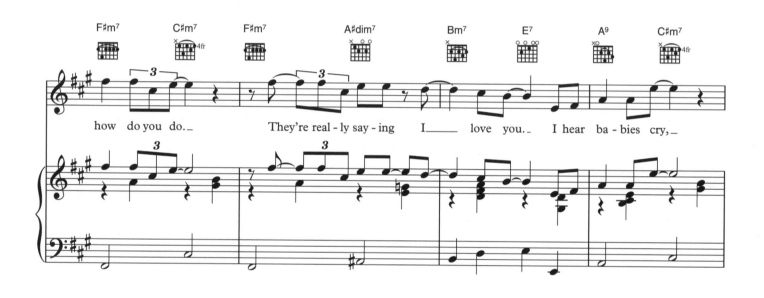

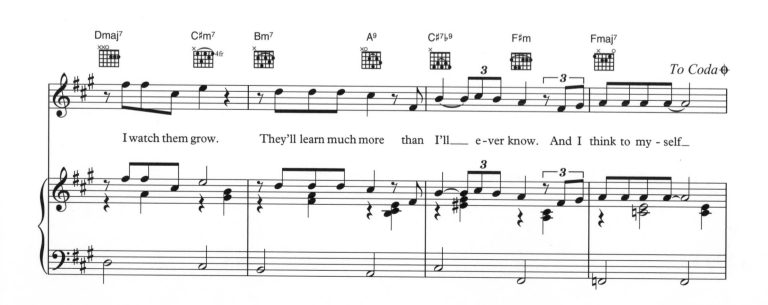

what a won - der - ful world.
Harmonica solo

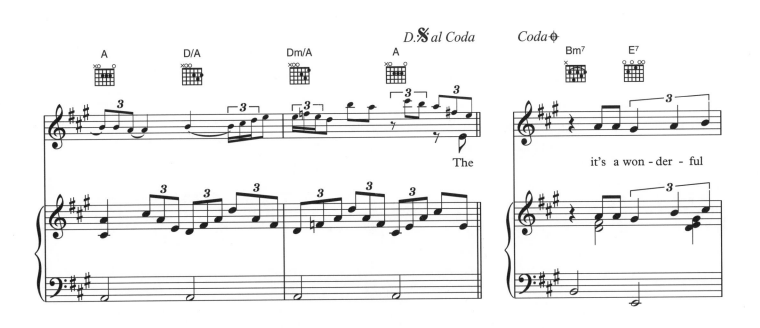

The

it's a won - der - ful

world.

I think to my-self___

rit.

what a won-der-ful

A tempo

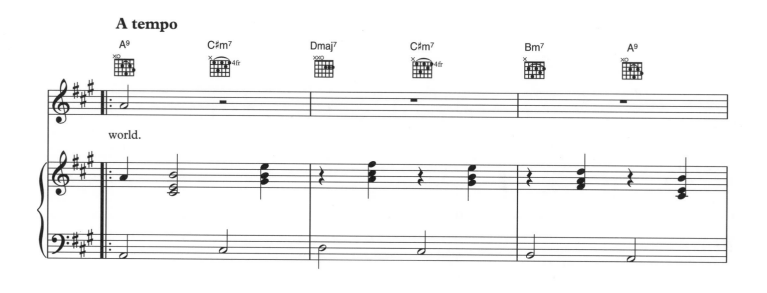

world.

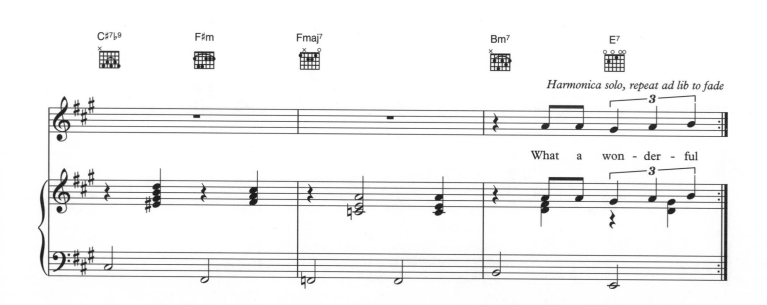

Harmonica solo, repeat ad lib to fade

What a won-der-ful

You Belong to Me

Words and Music by Pee Wee King, Redd Stewart and Chilton Price

See the py - ra - mids a - long the Nile,
See the mar - ket place in old Al - giers,

watch the sun - rise on a trop - ic isle.
send me pho - to - graphs and sou - ven - irs.

Just re - mem - ber darl - ing all the while,
But just re - mem - ber when a dream ap - pears,

you be - long to me.